It was Kipper's birthday.

Kipper wanted a party.

Everyone wanted to come.

Biff put up balloons.

Mum made a cake.

Dad took a sandwich.

"Stop it," said Mum.

Everyone came to the party.

Dad wanted to play a game.

But Kipper put the television on.

"Oh no!" said Mum. "What
a mess!"

The children played with
the bubbles.

"What a good party!"
everyone said.